HAL•LEONARD
JAZZ PLAY-ALONG

Book and CD for B♭, E♭, C and C Bass Clef Instruments

volume 40

Arranged and Produced by Mark Taylor

bossa nova

10 Latin Jazz Favourites

HLE
HAL LEONARD EUROPE
DISTRIBUTED BY MUSIC SALES

BOOK

TITLE	C Treble Instruments	B♭ Instruments	E♭ Instruments	C Bass Instruments
Bim Bom	6	24	42	60
Black Orpheus	8	26	44	62
Call Me	10	28	46	64
Estate	12	30	48	66
A Felicidade	14	32	50	68
Little Boat	7	25	43	61
A Man And A Woman (Un Homme Et Une Femme)	16	34	52	70
Only Trust Your Heart	18	36	54	72
Petite Fleur (Little Flower)	20	38	56	74
Song Of The Jet (Samba Do Avião)	22	40	58	76

CD

TITLE	CD Track Number Split Track / Melody	CD Track Number Full Stereo Track
Bim Bom	1	2
Black Orpheus	3	4
Call Me	5	6
Estate	7	8
A Felicidade	9	10
Little Boat	11	12
A Man And A Woman (Un Homme Et Une Femme)	13	14
Only Trust Your Heart	15	16
Petite Fleur (Little Flower)	17	18
Song Of The Jet (Samba Do Avião)	19	20
B♭ Tuning Notes		21

Published by
Hal Leonard Europe
A Music Sales / Hal Leonard Joint Venture Company
14-15 Berners Street, London W1T 3LJ, UK.

Exclusive Distributors:
Music Sales Limited
Distribution Centre, Newmarket Road, Bury St Edmunds, Suffolk IP33 3YB, UK.

Order No. HLE90003606
ISBN: 978-1-84772-647-2
This book © Copyright 2010 Hal Leonard Europe

Unauthorised reproduction of any part of this publication by any means including photocopying is an infringement of copyright.

Printed in the USA

Your Guarantee of Quality
As publishers, we strive to produce every book to the highest commercial standards.
The book has been carefully designed to minimise awkward page turns and to make playing from it a real pleasure.
Throughout, the printing and binding have been planned to ensure a sturdy, attractive publication which should give years of enjoyment.
If your copy fails to meet our high standards, please inform us and we will gladly replace it.

www.musicsales.com

Bossa Nova

HAL•LEONARD JAZZ PLAY-ALONG

Volume 40

Arranged and Produced by Mark Taylor

Featured Players:

Graham Breedlove–Trumpet
John Desalme–Tenor Sax
Tony Nalker–Piano
Jim Roberts–Bass & Guitar
Steve Fidyk & Dave McDonald–Drums

Recorded at Bias Studios, Springfield, Virginia, USA
Bob Dawson, Engineer

HOW TO USE THE CD:

Each song has two tracks:

1) Split Track/Melody

Woodwind, Brass, Keyboard, and **Mallet Players** can use this track as a learning tool for melody style and inflection.

Bass Players can learn and perform with this track – remove the recorded bass track by turning down the volume on the LEFT channel.

Keyboard and **Guitar Players** can learn and perform with this track – remove the recorded piano part by turning down the volume on the RIGHT channel.

2) Full Stereo Track

Soloists or **Groups** can learn and perform with this accompaniment track with the RHYTHM SECTION only.

CD

1 : SPLIT TRACK/MELODY
2 : FULL STEREO TRACK

BIM-BOM

WORDS AND MUSIC BY
JOAO GILBERTO

C VERSION

CD
11 : SPLIT TRACK/MELODY
12 : FULL STEREO TRACK

LITTLE BOAT

ORIGINAL WORDS BY RONALDO BOSCOLI
ENGLISH LYRICS BY BUDDY KAYE
MUSIC BY ROBERTO MENESCAL

C VERSION

BLACK ORPHEUS

WORDS AND MUSIC BY
LUIZ BONFA

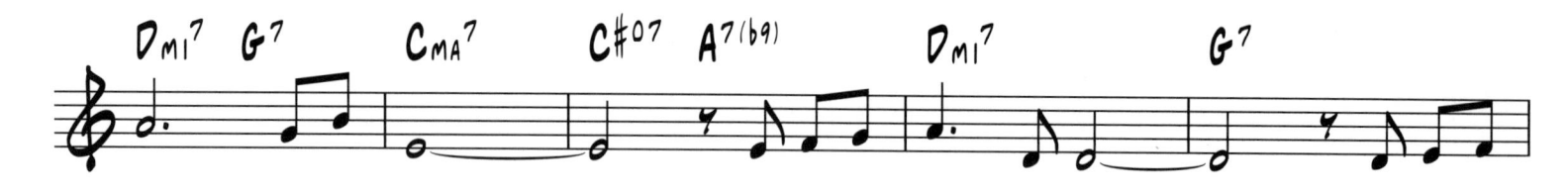

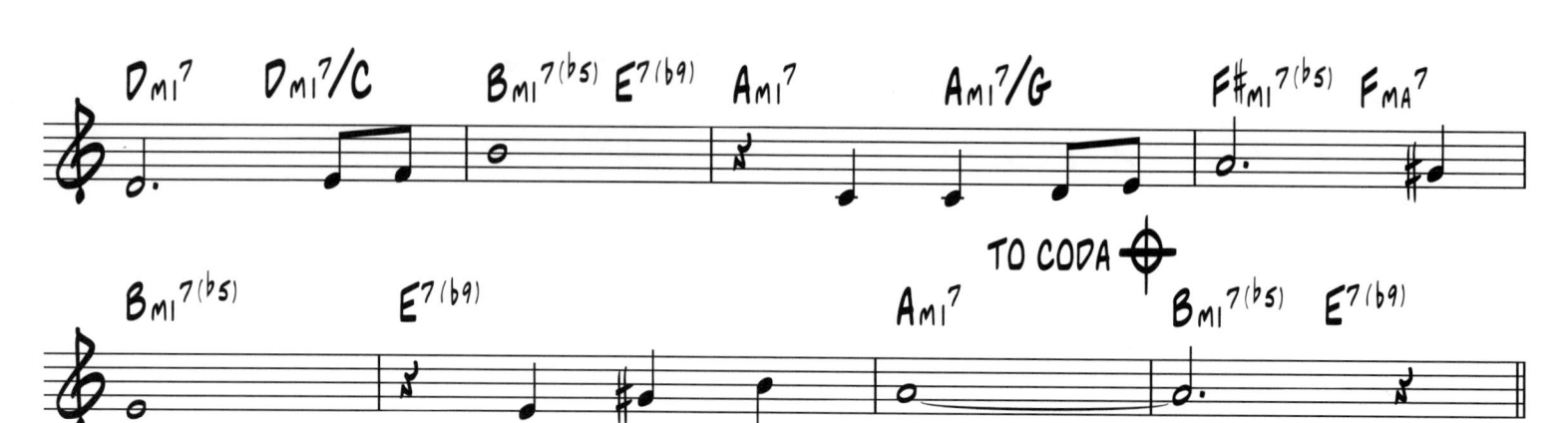

9

CALL ME

C Version

Words and Music by Tony Hatch

Bbmi7 Eb7sus Eb7 Abma7 Dbma7 Abma7
Dbma7 Abma7 Dbma7
TO CODA
Cma7 Dmi7 G7
SOLO
Cma7 Cmi7 F7sus F7 Bbma7 Bbmi7 Eb7sus Eb7
Abma7 Dbma7 Abma7 Dbma7 Abma7 Dbma7
1. Cma7
Dmi7 G7
2. Cma7 Dmi7 G7 Dmi7 G7 Cma7 F9(#11)
Emi7 Eb7 Dmi7 G7 Dmi7 G7 Cma7 D7sus D+7(b9) G7sus G7(b9)
Cma7 Cmi7 F7sus F7 Bbma7 Bbmi7
Eb7sus Eb7 Abma7 Dbma7 Abma7 Dbma7 Abma7 Dbma7
Cma7
D.S. AL CODA
CODA
3X'S Cma7 Db9(#11) Cma7

CD

7 : SPLIT TRACK/MELODY

8 : FULL STEREO TRACK

ESTATE

MUSIC BY BRUNO MARTINO
LYRICS BY BRUNO BRIGHETTI

C VERSION

A7 Eb7 DMI7 GMI7
3
A+7 A7 DMI7 GMI7 C7
FMA7 BbMA7 GMI7 EMI7
A7 Eb7 DMI7 DMI6 GMI7 A7
3
DMI7 DMI6 BbMA7 GMI7 Eb7 DMA7 EMI7
3
SOLO
A7 DMA7 GMI7 C7 FMA7 BbMA7
GMI7 EMI7 A7 Eb7 DMI7 GMI7
A+7 A7 DMI7 GMI7 C7 FMA7 BbMA7
GMI7 EMI7 A7 Eb7 DMI7 DMI6 GMI7
3
A7 DMI7 DMI6 GMI7 A7 DMI7

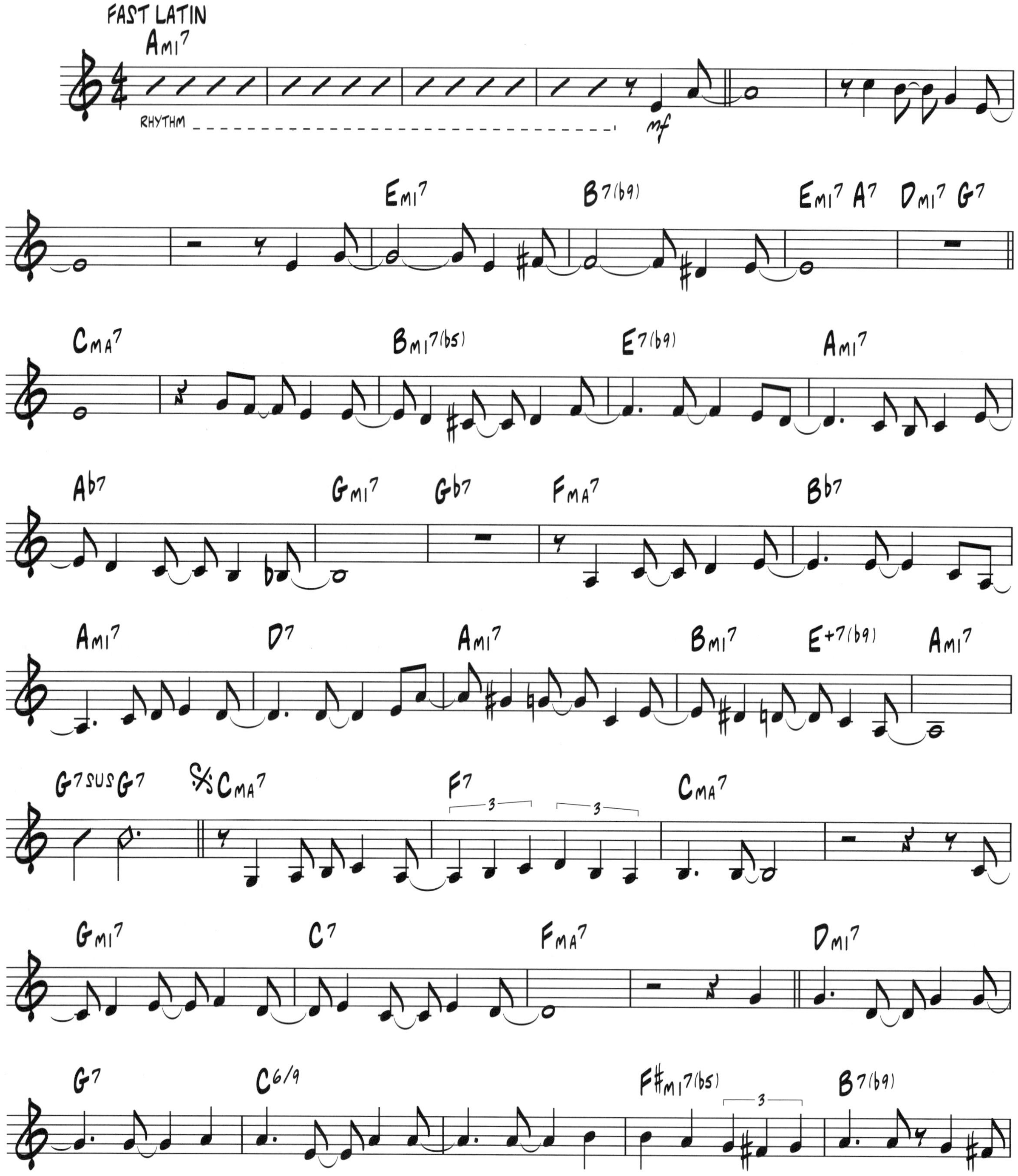

Emi7 A7 Dmi7 G7(b9) Ami7 Ami7/G D7/F#
TO CODA
Dmi7/F Ami7 Bmi7(b5) E+7(b9) Ami7
SOLO
Emi7 B7(b9) Emi7 A7 Dmi7 G7
Cma7 Bmi7(b5) E7(b9) Ami7 Ab7 Gmi7 Gb7
Fma7 Bb7 Ami7 D7 Ami7 Bmi7 E+7(b9) Ami7
G7sus G7 Cma7 F7 Cma7 Gmi7 C7
Fma7 Dmi7 G7 C6/9 F#mi7(b5)
B7(b9) Emi7 A7 Dmi7 G7(b9) Ami7 Ami7/G D7/F# Dmi7/F
D.S. AL CODA
Ami7 Bmi7(b5) E+7(b9) Ami7 G7sus G7
CODA
PLAY 3X'S
Ami7
Bmi7(b5) E+7(b9)
1., 2.
Ami7
3.
Ami7

A MAN AND A WOMAN
(UN HOMME ET UNE FEMME)
FROM A MAN AND A WOMAN

ORIGINAL WORDS BY PIERRE BAROUH
ENGLISH WORDS BY JERRY KELLER
MUSIC BY FRANCIS LAI

CD

◆13: SPLIT TRACK/MELODY
◆14: FULL STEREO TRACK

C VERSION

Copyright © 1966 EDITIONS SARAVAH, Paris, France
Copyright Renewed
This arrangement Copyright © 2005 EDITIONS SARAVAH, Paris, France
All Rights in the U.S. and Canada Controlled and Administered by UNIVERSAL MUSIC CORP.
All Rights Reserved   Used by Permission

D7SUS D7
DbMA7
GMI7
C7
FMA7
Bb7SUS
FMI7
E7(#11)
SOLO
EbMA7
D7SUS D7
D7SUS D7
DbMA7
GMI7
C7
FMA7
FMI7
Bb7
1.
EbMA7
E7(#11)
2.
EbMA7
Bb7SUS
FMI7
E7(#11)
D.S. AL CODA
CODA
FMA7
GMI7
C7
FMA7
GMI7
C7SUS
FMA7
EMA7
EbMA7
1.
EMA7
2.
EMA7
FMA7

ONLY TRUST YOUR HEART

WORDS BY SAMMY CAHN
MUSIC BY BENNY CARTER

C VERSION

LIGHT BOSSA

SOLO
CMA7 GMI7 Gb7 FMA7 B7 EMI7
AMI7 DMI7 G7 G+7
1.
CMA7 GMI7 C7
2.
C7 GMI7 Gb7 FMA7 C6/E DMI7
DMI7/C BMI7(b5) E+7 AMI7 GMI7 Gb7
FMA7 B7 EMI7 AMI7 DMI7
G7 G+7 Bb7 A7 DMI7 FMI7 Bb7
CMA7 EMI7 A7(b9) Ab7(b5) G7SUS G7(b9) CMA7
D.S. AL CODA
GMI7 Gb7
CODA
F#MI7(b5) FMI7
3
C6/E Eb7 DMI7 Db7(b5) CMA7
3

CD

17 : SPLIT TRACK/MELODY
18 : FULL STEREO TRACK

PETITE FLEUR

(LITTLE FLOWER)

BY SIDNEY BECHET

C VERSION

21

SONG OF THE JET
(SAMBA DO AVIÃO)

ENGLISH LYRIC BY GENE LEES
ORIGINAL TEXT AND MUSIC BY ANTONIO CARLOS JOBIM

C VERSION

GMI7(b5) C+7(b9) FMI7
TO CODA F7 E+7
SOLO
EbMA7 Gb07 FMI7 Gb07 GMI7 G+7 AbMA7
AbMI6 GMI7 Gb07 GMI7(b5) C+7(b9) F7
Bb7 EbMA7/G Gb07 FMI7 Gb07 GMI7
G+7 AbMA7 AbMI6 AbMA7 AbMI6 EbMA7/G Gb07
AbMA7 AbMI6 GMI7(b5) C+7(b9) FMI7(b5) Bb7(b9) GMI7(b5) C+7(b9)
FMI7 F7 E+7 D.S. AL CODA
CODA F7 E7(b5) EbMA7 EMA7 EbMA7

CD

1: SPLIT TRACK/MELODY
2: FULL STEREO TRACK

BIM BOM

WORDS AND MUSIC BY
JOAO GILBERTO

B♭ VERSION

Little Boat

Original words by Ronaldo Boscoli
English lyrics by Buddy Kaye
Music by Roberto Menescal

Bb Version

Medium Bossa

CD
3 : SPLIT TRACK/MELODY
4 : FULL STEREO TRACK

BLACK ORPHEUS

WORDS AND MUSIC BY
LUIZ BONFA

B♭ VERSION

SOLO
BMI7 C#MI7(b5) F#7(b9) BMI7 C#MI7(b5) F#7(b9)
BMI7 EMI7 A7 DMA7 D#o7 B7(b9)
EMI7 A7 DMA7 GMA7
C#MI7(b5) F#7(b9) BMI7 C#MI7(b5) F#7(b9)
BMI7 C#MI7(b5) F#7(b9) BMI7 C#MI7(b5) F#7(b9)
F#MI7(b5) B7(b9) EMI7
(EMI7) EMI7/D C#MI7(b5) F#7(b9) BMI7 BMI7/A G#MI7(b5) GMA7
D.S. AL CODA
C#MI7(b5) F#7(b9) BMI7 C#MI7(b5) F#7(b9)
mf
CODA
BMI7 EMI7 BMI7 EMI7 BMI7 EMI7 F#MI7
BMI7 EMI7 A13 D6/9 GMA7 C#7(b9) F#7(#9) BMI7
RIT.

CD
5 : SPLIT TRACK/MELODY
6 : FULL STEREO TRACK

CALL ME

WORDS AND MUSIC BY
TONY HATCH

B♭ VERSION

CMI7 F7SUS F7 B♭MA7 E♭MA7 B♭MA7
E♭MA7 B♭MA7 E♭MA7 TO CODA DMA7 EMI7 A7
SOLO
DMA7 DMI7 G7SUS G7 CMA7 CMI7 F7SUS F7
B♭MA7 E♭MA7 B♭MA7 E♭MA7 B♭MA7 E♭MA7 1. DMA7
EMI7 A7 2. DMA7 EMI7 A7 EMI7 A7 DMA7 G9(♯11)
F♯MI7 F7 EMI7 A7 EMI7 A7 DMA7 E7SUS E+7(♭9) A7SUS A7(♭9)
DMA7 DMI7 G7SUS G7 CMA7 CMI7
F7SUS F7 B♭MA7 E♭MA7 B♭MA7 E♭MA7 B♭MA7 E♭MA7
DMA7 D.S. AL CODA
CODA
3X'S DMA7 E♭9(♯11) DMA7

CD

7 : SPLIT TRACK/MELODY
8 : FULL STEREO TRACK

ESTATE

MUSIC BY BRUNO MARTINO
LYRICS BY BRUNO BRIGHETTI

B♭ VERSION

B7 F7 Emi7 Ami7
B+7 B7 Emi7 Ami7 D7
Gma7 Cma7 Ami7 F#mi7
B7 F7 Emi7 Emi6 Ami7 B7
SOLO
Emi7 Emi6 Cma7 Ami7 F7 Ema7 F#mi7
B7 Ema7 Ami7 D7 Gma7 Cma7
Ami7 F#mi7 B7 F7 Emi7 Ami7
B+7 B7 Emi7 Ami7 D7 Gma7 Cma7
Ami7 F#mi7 B7 F7 Emi7 Emi6 Ami7
B7 Emi7 Emi6 Ami7 B7 Emi7

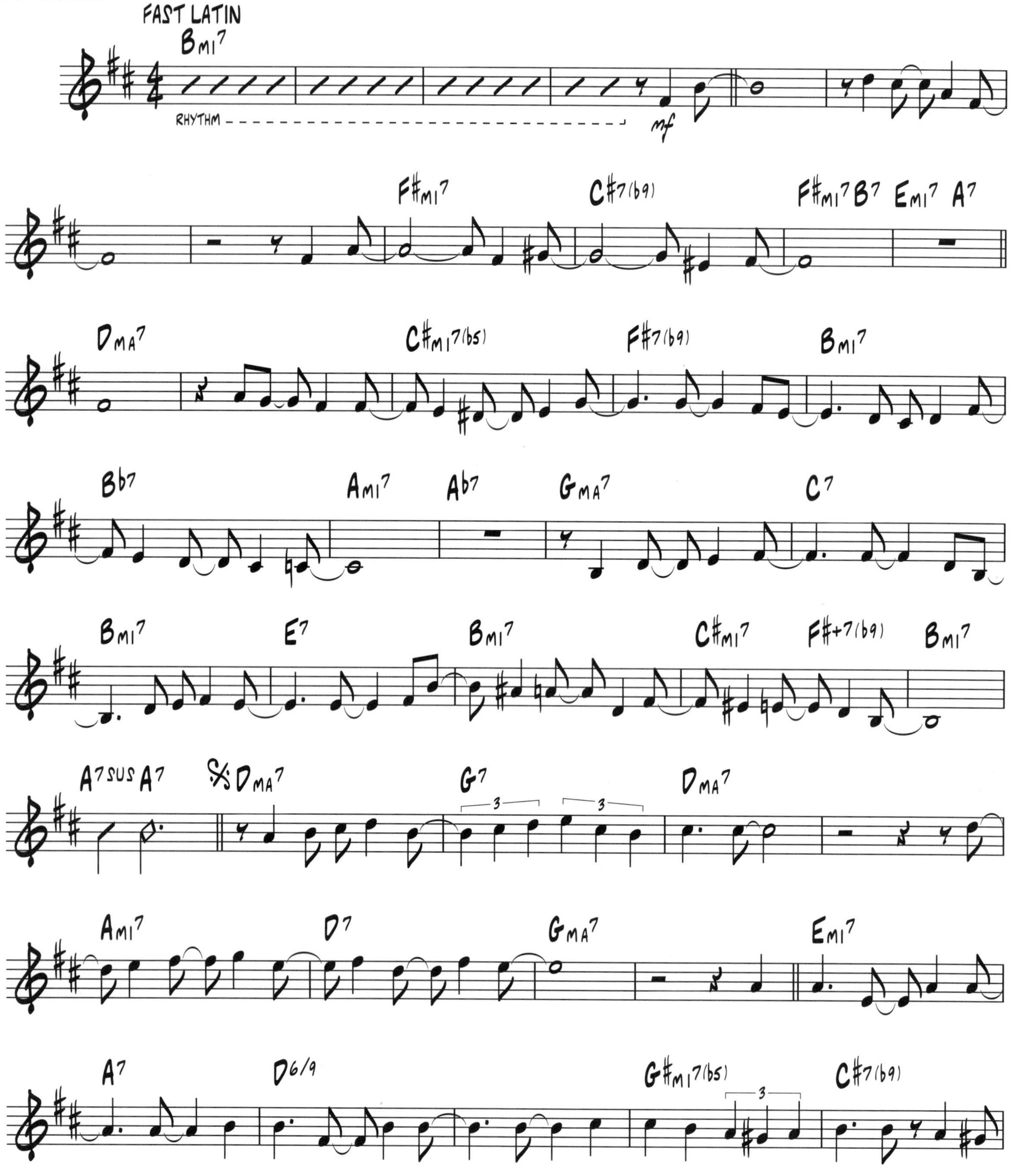

F#MI7 B7 EMI7 A7(b9) BMI7 BMI7/A E7/G#
TO CODA
EMI7/G BMI7 C#MI7(b5) F#+7(b9) BMI7
SOLO
F#MI7 C#7(b9) F#MI7 B7 EMI7 A7
DMA7 C#MI7(b5) F#7(b9) BMI7 Bb7 AMI7 Ab7
GMA7 C7 BMI7 E7 BMI7 C#MI7 F#+7(b9) BMI7
A7SUS A7 DMA7 G7 DMA7 AMI7 D7
GMA7 EMI7 A7 D6/9 G#MI7(b5)
C#7(b9) F#MI7 B7 EMI7 A7(b9) BMI7 BMI7/A E7/G# EMI7/G
BMI7 C#MI7(b5) F#+7(b9) BMI7 A7SUS A7
D.S. AL CODA
CODA
PLAY 3X'S
BMI7
C#MI7(b5) F#+7(b9)
1., 2.
BMI7
3.
BMI7

CD

13 : SPLIT TRACK/MELODY
14 : FULL STEREO TRACK

A MAN AND A WOMAN

(UN HOMME ET UNE FEMME)

FROM A MAN AND A WOMAN

ORIGINAL WORDS BY PIERRE BAROUH
ENGLISH WORDS BY JERRY KELLER
MUSIC BY FRANCIS LAI

B♭ VERSION

E7SUS E7
E♭MA7
AMI7 D7 GMA7 C7SUS GMI7 F♯7(♯11)
SOLO
FMA7 E7SUS E7 E7SUS E7 E♭MA7
AMI7 D7 GMA7
GMI7 C7 1. FMA7 F♯7(♯11)
D.S. AL CODA
2. FMA7 C7SUS GMI7 F♯7(♯11)
CODA
GMA7 AMI7 D7
GMA7 AMI7 D7SUS
GMA7 F♯MA7 FMA7
1. F♯MA7
2. F♯MA7 GMA7

CD

15 : SPLIT TRACK/MELODY

16 : FULL STEREO TRACK

ONLY TRUST YOUR HEART

WORDS BY SAMMY CAHN
MUSIC BY BENNY CARTER

B♭ VERSION

DMA7 AMI7 Ab7
SOLO
GMA7 C#7 F#MI7
BMI7 EMI7 A7 A+7
1.
DMA7 AMI7 D7
2.
D7 AMI7 Ab7 GMA7 D6/F# EMI7
EMI7/D C#MI7(b5) F#+7 BMI7 AMI7 Ab7
GMA7 C#7 F#MI7 BMI7 EMI7
A7 A+7 C7 B7 EMI7 GMI7 C7
DMA7 F#MI7 B7(b9) Bb7(b5) A7SUS A7(b9) DMA7
D.S. AL CODA
AMI7 Ab7
CODA
G#MI7(b5) GMI7
3
D6/F# F7
3
EMI7 Eb7(b5) DMA7

CD

17 : SPLIT TRACK/MELODY
18 : FULL STEREO TRACK

PETITE FLEUR
(LITTLE FLOWER)

BY SIDNEY BECHET

B♭ VERSION

39

CD

19 : SPLIT TRACK/MELODY
20 : FULL STEREO TRACK

SONG OF THE JET
(SAMBA DO AVIÃO)

ENGLISH LYRIC BY GENE LEES
ORIGINAL TEXT AND MUSIC BY ANTONIO CARLOS JOBIM

Bb VERSION

Am7(b5)   D+7(b9)   Gm7

TO CODA ⊕ G7   F#+7

SOLO
Fma7   Ab°7   Gm7   Ab°7   Am7   A+7   Bbma7

Bbmi6   Am7   Ab°7   Am7(b5)   D+7(b9)   G7

C7   Fma7/A   Ab°7   Gm7   Ab°7   Am7

A+7   Bbma7   Bbmi6   Bbma7   Bbmi6   Fma7/A   Ab°7

Bbma7   Bbmi6   Am7(b5) D+7(b9)   Gm7(b5) C7(b9)   Am7(b5)   D+7(b9)

Gm7   G7   F#+7   D.S. AL CODA

⊕ CODA
G7   F#7(b5)   Fma7   F#ma7   Fma7

CD

1: SPLIT TRACK/MELODY
2: FULL STEREO TRACK

BIM-BOM

WORDS AND MUSIC BY
JOAO GILBERTO

E♭ VERSION

CD

11 : SPLIT TRACK/MELODY

12 : FULL STEREO TRACK

LITTLE BOAT

ORIGINAL WORDS BY RONALDO BOSCOLI
ENGLISH LYRICS BY BUDDY KAYE
MUSIC BY ROBERTO MENESCAL

E♭ VERSION

CD

3: SPLIT TRACK/MELODY

4: FULL STEREO TRACK

BLACK ORPHEUS

WORDS AND MUSIC BY
LUIZ BONFA

E♭ VERSION

SOLO
F#MI7 | G#MI7(b5) C#7(b9) | F#MI7 | G#MI7(b5) C#7(b9)
F#MI7 | BMI7 E7 | AMA7 | A#o7 F#7(b9)
BMI7 | E7 | AMA7 | DMA7
G#MI7(b5) | C#7(b9) | F#MI7 | G#MI7(b5) C#7(b9)
F#MI7 | G#MI7(b5) C#7(b9) | F#MI7 | G#MI7(b5) C#7(b9)
C#MI7(b5) | F#7(b9) | BMI7 |
(BMI7) BMI7/A | G#MI7(b5) C#7(b9) | F#MI7 F#MI7/E | D#MI7(b5) DMA7
D.S. AL CODA
G#MI7(b5) | C#7(b9) | F#MI7 | G#MI7(b5) C#7(b9)
mf
CODA
F#MI7 | BMI7 F#MI7 | BMI7 F#MI7 | BMI7 C#MI7
F#MI7 | BMI7 E13 | A6/9 DMA7 | G#7(b9) C#7(#9) | F#MI7
RIT.

CD

5 : SPLIT TRACK/MELODY

6 : FULL STEREO TRACK

E♭ VERSION

CALL ME

WORDS AND MUSIC BY
TONY HATCH

GMI7 C7SUS C7 FMA7 B♭MA7 FMA7
B♭MA7 FMA7 B♭MA7 TO CODA AMA7 BMI7 E7
SOLO
AMA7 AMI7 D7SUS D7 GMA7 GMI7 C7SUS C7
FMA7 B♭MA7 FMA7 B♭MA7 FMA7 B♭MA7 1. AMA7
BMI7 E7 2. AMA7 BMI7 E7 BMI7 E7 AMA7 D9(♯11)
C♯MI7 C7 BMI7 E7 BMI7 E7 AMA7 B7SUS B+7(♭9) E7SUS E7(♭9)
AMA7 AMI7 D7SUS D7 GMA7 GMI7
C7SUS C7 FMA7 B♭MA7 FMA7 B♭MA7 FMA7 B♭MA7
AMA7 D.S. AL CODA
CODA 3X'S AMA7 B♭9(♯11) AMA7

CD

7 : SPLIT TRACK/MELODY

8 : FULL STEREO TRACK

ESTATE

MUSIC BY BRUNO MARTINO
LYRICS BY BRUNO BRIGHETTI

E♭ VERSION

49

CD
9: SPLIT TRACK/MELODY
10: FULL STEREO TRACK

A FELICIDADE

WORDS AND MUSIC BY VINICIUS DE MORAES,
ANDRE SALVET AND ANTONIO CARLOS JOBIM

Eb VERSION

C#MI7 F#7 BMI7 E7(b9) F#MI7 F#MI7/E B7/D#
TO CODA
BMI7/D F#MI7 G#MI7(b5) C#+7(b9) F#MI7
SOLO
C#MI7 G#7(b9) C#MI7 F#7 BMI7 E7
AMA7 G#MI7(b5) C#7(b9) F#MI7 F7 EMI7 Eb7
DMA7 G7 F#MI7 B7 F#MI7 G#MI7 C#+7(b9) F#MI7
E7SUS E7 AMA7 D7 AMA7 EMI7 A7
DMA7 BMI7 E7 A6/9 D#MI7(b5)
G#7(b9) C#MI7 F#7 BMI7 E7(b9) F#MI7 F#MI7/E B7/D# BMI7/D
F#MI7 G#MI7(b5) C#+7(b9) F#MI7 E7SUS E7
D.S. AL CODA
CODA
PLAY 3X'S
F#MI7
G#MI7(b5) C#+7(b9)
1., 2.
F#MI7
3.
F#MI7

CD

13: SPLIT TRACK/MELODY
14: FULL STEREO TRACK

Eb VERSION

A MAN AND A WOMAN

(UN HOMME ET UNE FEMME)

FROM A MAN AND A WOMAN

ORIGINAL WORDS BY PIERRE BAROUH
ENGLISH WORDS BY JERRY KELLER
MUSIC BY FRANCIS LAI

B7SUS B7
B♭MA7
EMI7 A7 DMA7 G7SUS DMI7 C♯7(♯11)
SOLO
CMA7 B7SUS B7 B7SUS B7 B♭MA7
EMI7 A7 DMA7
DMI7 G7 1. CMA7 C♯7(♯11)
D.S. AL CODA
2. CMA7 G7SUS DMI7 C♯7(♯11)
CODA
DMA7 EMI7 A7
DMA7 EMI7 A7SUS
DMA7 C♯MA7 CMA7
1. C♯MA7
2. C♯MA7 DMA7

CD

15 : SPLIT TRACK/MELODY

16 : FULL STEREO TRACK

ONLY TRUST YOUR HEART

WORDS BY SAMMY CAHN
MUSIC BY BENNY CARTER

E♭ VERSION

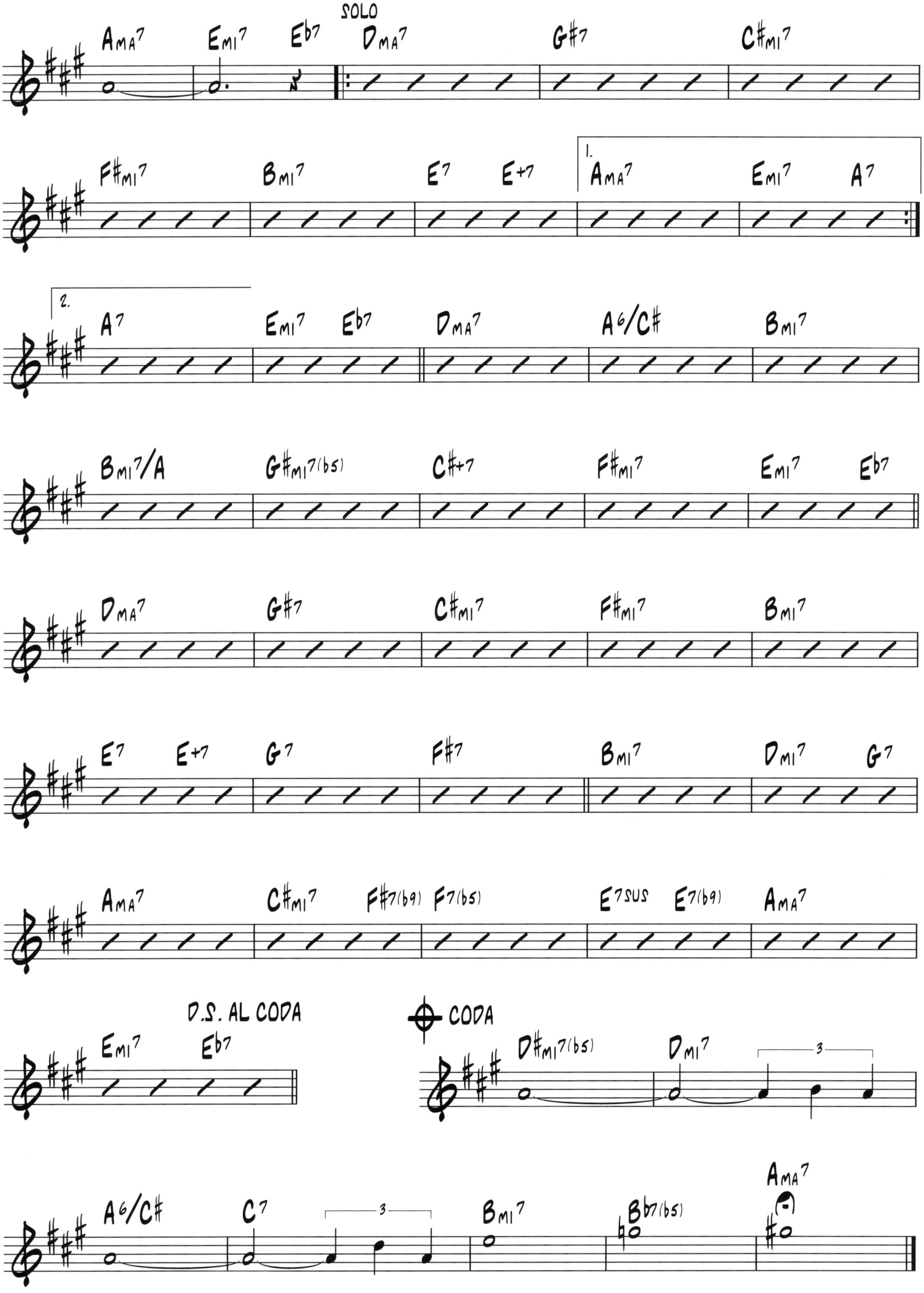
SOLO
AMA7 EMI7 Eb7 DMA7 G#7 C#MI7
F#MI7 BMI7 E7 E+7
1.
AMA7 EMI7 A7
2.
A7 EMI7 Eb7 DMA7 A6/C# BMI7
BMI7/A G#MI7(b5) C#+7 F#MI7 EMI7 Eb7
DMA7 G#7 C#MI7 F#MI7 BMI7
E7 E+7 G7 F#7 BMI7 DMI7 G7
AMA7 C#MI7 F#7(b9) F7(b5) E7SUS E7(b9) AMA7
D.S. AL CODA
EMI7 Eb7
CODA
D#MI7(b5) DMI7
3
A6/C# C7
3
BMI7 Bb7(b5) AMA7

CD

17: SPLIT TRACK/MELODY
18: FULL STEREO TRACK

PETITE FLEUR
(LITTLE FLOWER)

BY SIDNEY BECHET

Eb VERSION

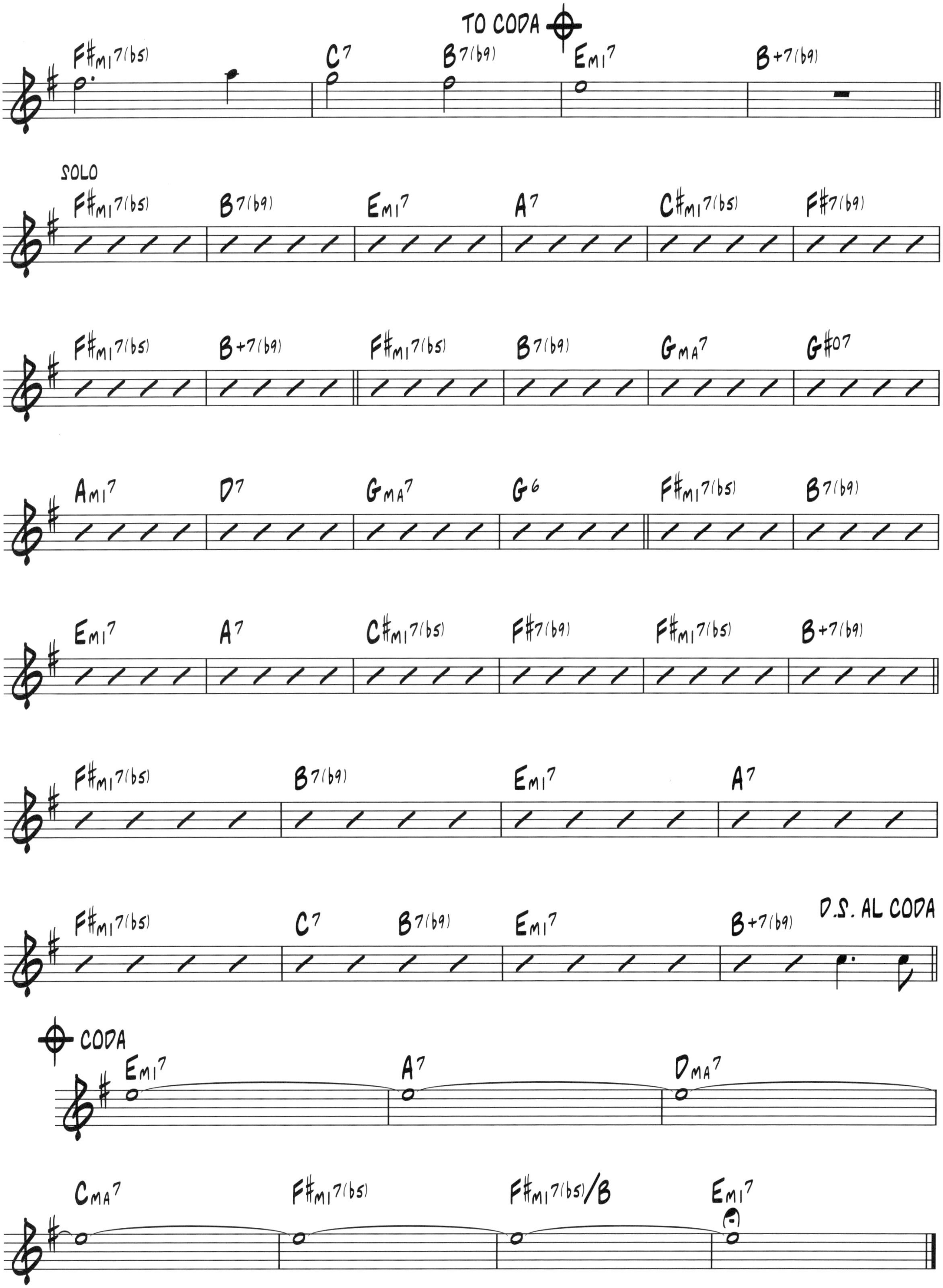
TO CODA
F#MI7(b5) C7 B7(b9) EMI7 B+7(b9)
SOLO
F#MI7(b5) B7(b9) EMI7 A7 C#MI7(b5) F#7(b9)
F#MI7(b5) B+7(b9) F#MI7(b5) B7(b9) GMA7 G#07
AMI7 D7 GMA7 G6 F#MI7(b5) B7(b9)
EMI7 A7 C#MI7(b5) F#7(b9) F#MI7(b5) B+7(b9)
F#MI7(b5) B7(b9) EMI7 A7
F#MI7(b5) C7 B7(b9) EMI7 B+7(b9) D.S. AL CODA
CODA
EMI7 A7 DMA7
CMA7 F#MI7(b5) F#MI7(b5)/B EMI7

CD

19 : SPLIT TRACK/MELODY
20 : FULL STEREO TRACK

SONG OF THE JET

(SAMBA DO AVIÃO)

ENGLISH LYRIC BY GENE LEES
ORIGINAL TEXT AND MUSIC BY ANTONIO CARLOS JOBIM

E♭ VERSION

SAMBA

EMI7(b5) A+7(b9) DMI7
TO CODA D7 C#+7
SOLO
CMA7 Eb07 DMI7 Eb07 EMI7 E+7 FMA7
FMI6 EMI7 Eb07 EMI7(b5) A+7(b9) D7
G7 CMA7/E Eb07 DMI7 Eb07 EMI7
E+7 FMA7 FMI6 FMA7 FMI6 CMA7/E Eb07
FMA7 FMI6 EMI7(b5) A+7(b9) DMI7(b5) G7(b9) EMI7(b5) A+7(b9)
DMI7 D7 C#+7 D.S. AL CODA
CODA
D7 C#7(b5) CMA7 C#MA7 CMA7

CD

1: SPLIT TRACK/MELODY

2: FULL STEREO TRACK

BIM-BOM

WORDS AND MUSIC BY
JOAO GILBERTO

C VERSION

CD

11 : SPLIT TRACK/MELODY

12 : FULL STEREO TRACK

LITTLE BOAT

ORIGINAL WORDS BY RONALDO BOSCOLI
ENGLISH LYRICS BY BUDDY KAYE
MUSIC BY ROBERTO MENESCAL

CD

3 : SPLIT TRACK/MELODY

4 : FULL STEREO TRACK

BLACK ORPHEUS

WORDS AND MUSIC BY
LUIZ BONFA

𝄢: C VERSION

SOLO
AMI7 BMI7(b5) E7(b9) AMI7 BMI7(b5) E7(b9)
AMI7 DMI7 G7 CMA7 C#07 A7(b9)
DMI7 G7 CMA7 FMA7
BMI7(b5) E7(b9) AMI7 BMI7(b5) E7(b9)
AMI7 BMI7(b5) E7(b9) AMI7 BMI7(b5) E7(b9)
EMI7(b5) A7(b9) DMI7
(DMI7) DMI7/C BMI7(b5) E7(b9) AMI7 AMI7/G F#MI7(b5) FMA7
D.S. AL CODA
BMI7(b5) E7(b9) AMI7 BMI7(b5) E7(b9)
mf
CODA
AMI7 DMI7 AMI7 DMI7 AMI7 DMI7 EMI7
AMI7 DMI7 G13 C6/9 FMA7 B7(b9) E7(#9) AMI7
RIT.

CD

5 : SPLIT TRACK/MELODY

6 : FULL STEREO TRACK

CALL ME

WORDS AND MUSIC BY
TONY HATCH

C VERSION

65

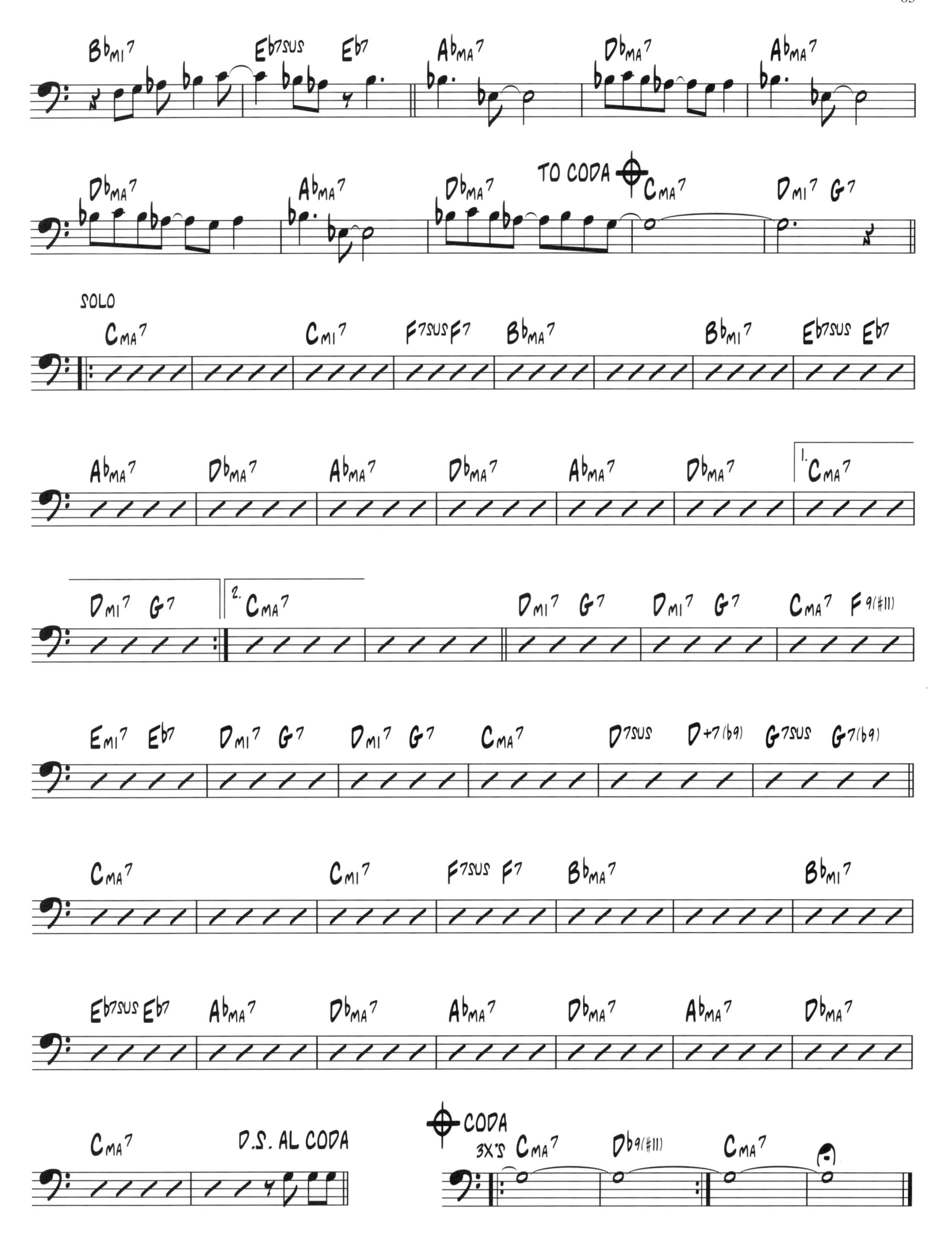

ESTATE

MUSIC BY BRUNO MARTINO
LYRICS BY BRUNO BRIGHETTI

C VERSION

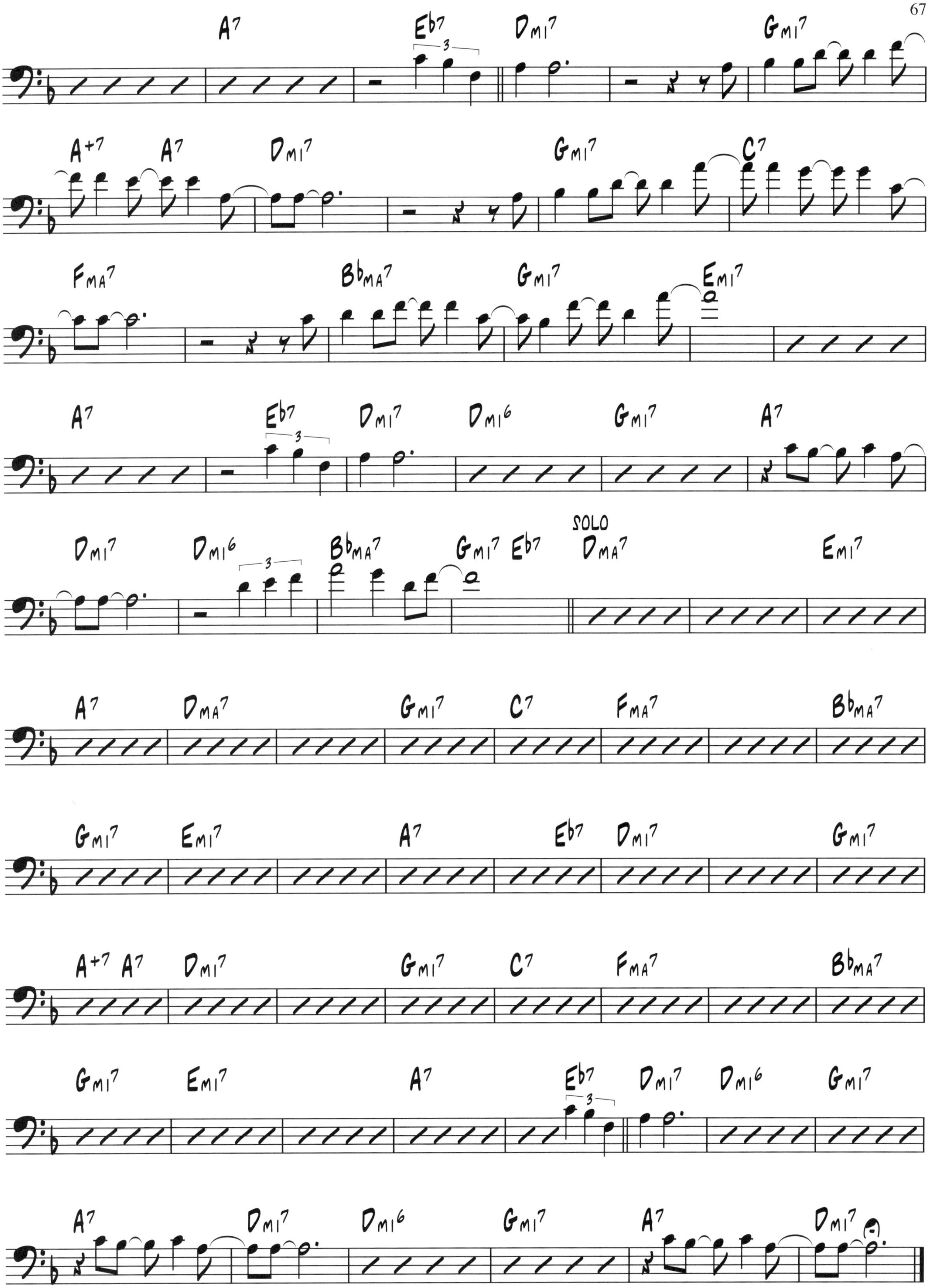

A Felicidade

WORDS AND MUSIC BY VINICIUS DE MORAES,
ANDRE SALVET AND ANTONIO CARLOS JOBIM

C VERSION
FAST LATIN

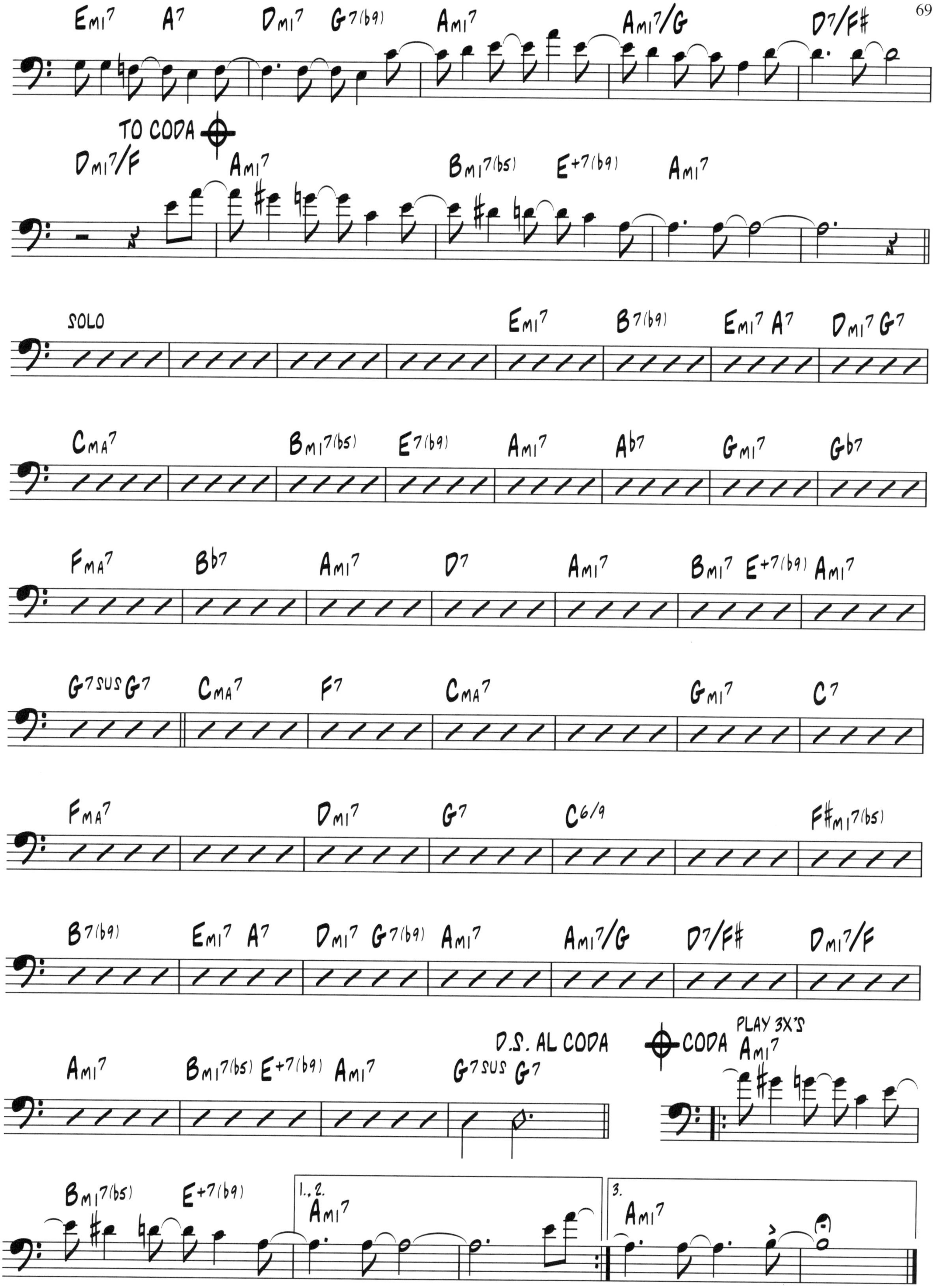

CD

13: SPLIT TRACK/MELODY

14: FULL STEREO TRACK

A MAN AND A WOMAN

(UN HOMME ET UNE FEMME)

FROM A MAN AND A WOMAN

ORIGINAL WORDS BY PIERRE BAROUH
ENGLISH WORDS BY JERRY KELLER
MUSIC BY FRANCIS LAI

𝄢: C VERSION

D7SUS D7
D♭MA7
GMI7 C7 FMA7 B♭7SUS FMI7 E7(♯11)
SOLO
E♭MA7 D7SUS D7 D7SUS D7 D♭MA7
GMI7 C7 FMA7
FMI7 B♭7 E♭MA7 E7(♯11)
D.S. AL CODA
E♭MA7 B♭7SUS FMI7 E7(♯11)
CODA
FMA7 GMI7 C7
FMA7 GMI7 C7SUS
FMA7 EMA7 E♭MA7
EMA7 EMA7 FMA7

ONLY TRUST YOUR HEART

WORDS BY SAMMY CAHN
MUSIC BY BENNY CARTER

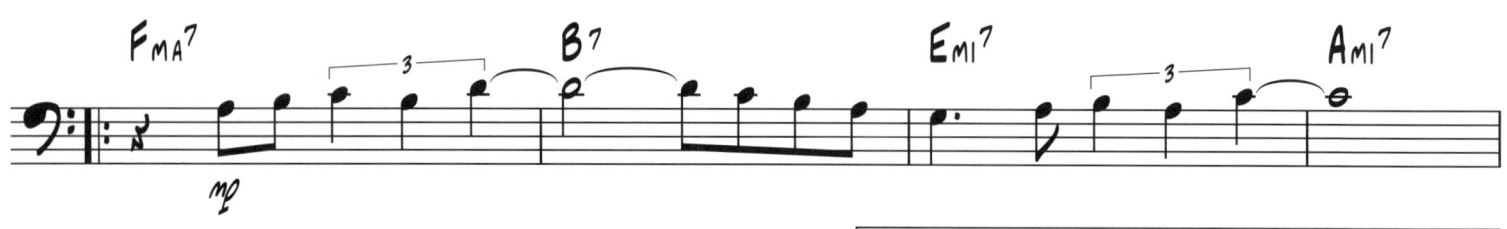

C VERSION
LIGHT BOSSA

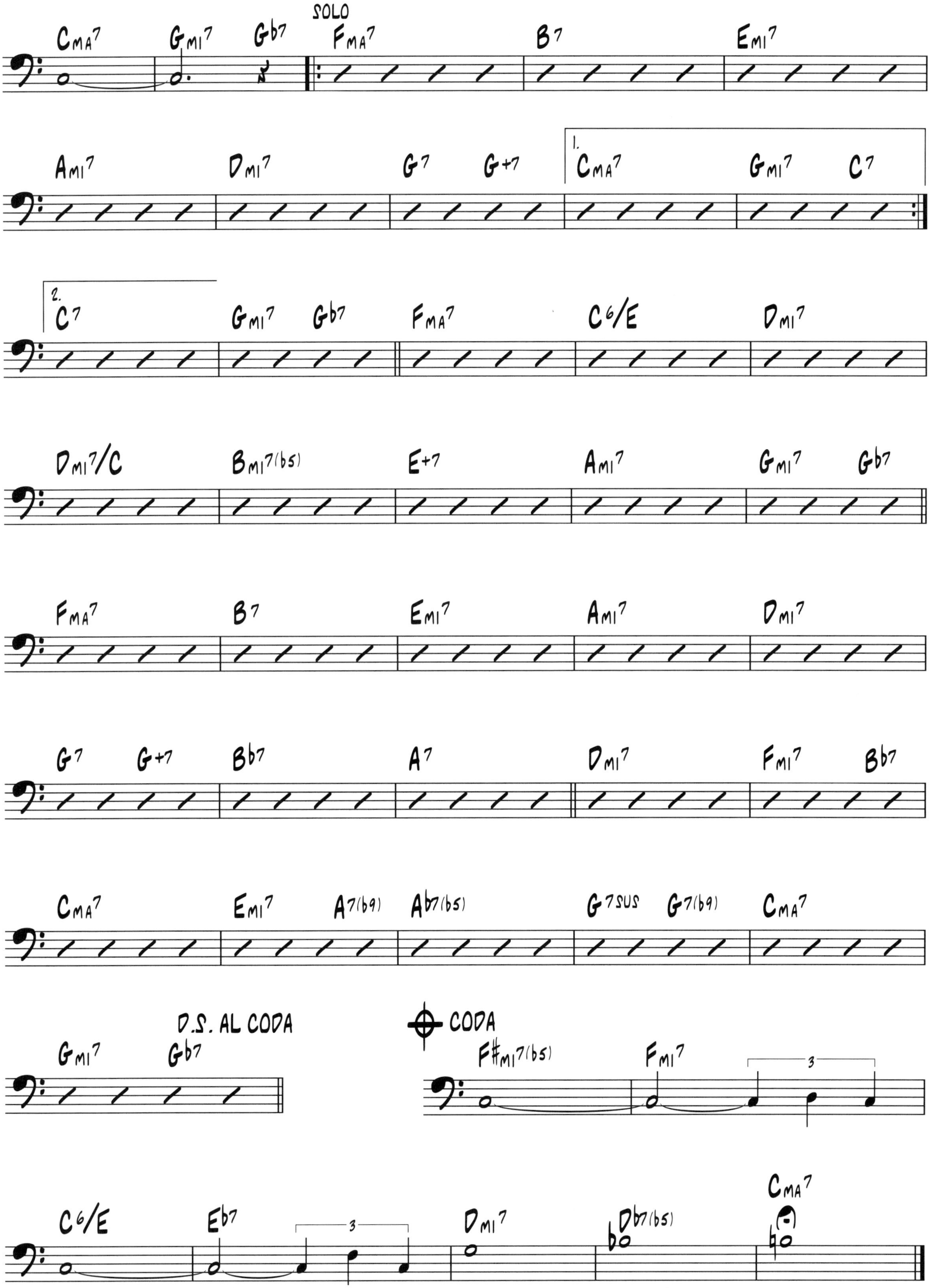

CD

17: SPLIT TRACK/MELODY

18: FULL STEREO TRACK

PETITE FLEUR
(LITTLE FLOWER)

BY SIDNEY BECHET

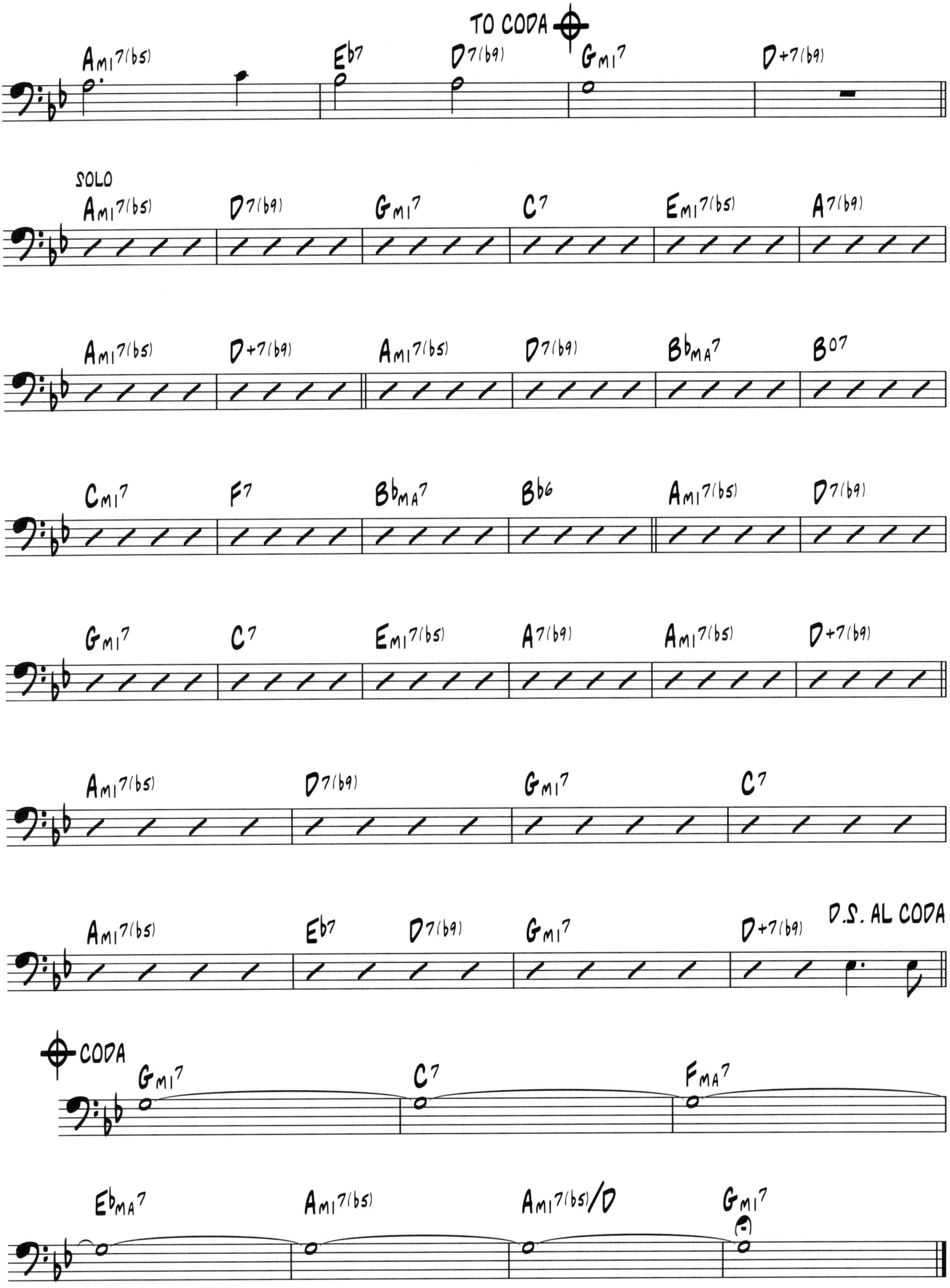
TO CODA
AMI7(b5) Eb7 D7(b9) GMI7 D+7(b9)
SOLO
AMI7(b5) D7(b9) GMI7 C7 EMI7(b5) A7(b9)
AMI7(b5) D+7(b9) AMI7(b5) D7(b9) BbMA7 B°7
CMI7 F7 BbMA7 Bb6 AMI7(b5) D7(b9)
GMI7 C7 EMI7(b5) A7(b9) AMI7(b5) D+7(b9)
AMI7(b5) D7(b9) GMI7 C7
AMI7(b5) Eb7 D7(b9) GMI7 D+7(b9)
D.S. AL CODA
CODA
GMI7 C7 FMA7
EbMA7 AMI7(b5) AMI7(b5)/D GMI7

Song of the Jet
(Samba do Avião)

English Lyric by Gene Lees
Original Text and Music by Antonio Carlos Jobim

Gmi7(b5) C+7(b9) Fmi7
TO CODA F7 E+7
SOLO
Ebma7 Gbo7 Fmi7 Gbo7 Gmi7 G+7 Abma7
Abmi6 Gmi7 Gbo7 Gmi7(b5) C+7(b9) F7
Bb7 Ebma7/G Gbo7 Fmi7 Gbo7 Gmi7
G+7 Abma7 Abmi6 Abma7 Abmi6 Ebma7/G Gbo7
Abma7 Abmi6 Gmi7(b5) C+7(b9) Fmi7(b5) Bb7(b9) Gmi7(b5) C+7(b9)
Fmi7 F7 E+7 D.S. AL CODA
CODA
F7 E7(b5) Ebma7 Ema7 Ebma7